NEW PIECES FOR CLARINET: BOOK

GRADES 5 & 6

CLARINET PARTS WANTED
DANCE PIECE.

FREDERICK THURSTON
TECHNICAL STUDY
IN D

© 1978 by The Associated Board of the Royal Schools of Music
14 Bedford Square, London WC1B 3JG

Printed in England
A.B.1660

2.95

SICILIANO

Gordon Jacob

ALMOST A WALTZ

David Lyon

6

A.B. 1660

MARCHE EN RONDEAU

Terence Greaves

11

A.B. 1660

12

A.B. 1660

senza ped.

ROUND DANCE

Raymond Warren

A.B. 1660

ARIOSO

Sebastian Forbes

DANCE PIECE

Arthur Wills

26

The Associated Board's series of new
pieces for wind instruments covers Grades 3—6.
Two books are available for each instrument:
bassoon, clarinet, flute and oboe.

For further details of these pieces
and for a list of all the Board's publications,
please write to the Publishing Department,
14 Bedford Square, London WC1B 3JG.